Arithmetricks

by

JEROME S. MEYER

SCHOLASTIC BOOK SERVICES

Published by Scholastic Book Services, a division
of Scholastic Magazines, Inc., New York, N. Y.

To

SHARON KOLODNY

a very bright and talented young lady

CONTENTS

Foreword

Few things are more fascinating than numbers when you start playing around with them. The tricks you can do with numbers are utterly bewildering. Many of them are described in this little book. Be sure your understand them before you present them to your friends, because the better able you are to do them the more mysterious they become.

Numbers have personalities just the same as people. Some people are witty and interesting, while others are dull and uninteresting. And so it is with numbers. The number 1, for example, is the *only* number which remains the same when raised to any power or when any root is taken. No matter how many times you multiply 1 by itself, the result will always be 1—and that can be said of no other number.

Then there is number 2. This is the *only* even number that is also a prime number. A prime number, by definition, is any number without factors; it is divisible only by itself and 1, so no even number except 2 can ever be prime.

Also note that 2 and 6 are the only numbers whose factors, when multiplied, equal their sum:

$$2 + 2 = 4 \quad \text{and} \quad 2 \times 2 = 4$$
$$1 + 2 + 3 = 6 \quad \text{and} \quad 1 \times 2 \times 3 = 6$$

We could go on and on, taking more numbers and showing them off, but that would take too long. You will see for yourself, after going through *Arithmetricks*, how remarkable numbers really are.

J. S. M.

Mathelepathy

M ATHELEPATHY is a combination of mathematics and telepathy. In the following amazing tricks, you are to write a number on a piece of paper, fold the paper, and hide it until the time comes to produce it. You then tell a friend to add or multiply numbers entirely of his own choice and show you the result. When he does this, you produce the hidden number and amaze him.

There are very few tricks in arithmetic that can produce the bewilderment and utter amazement that come from performing mathelepathy. Of course, performance improves with practice, so it is advisable to do these tricks several times by yourself before you try them on your friends.

The 3937 Trick

What You Do	*What Your Friend Does*
1. Write the number 3937 on a piece of paper; fold it and hide it.	
2. Tell your friend to write down the year he was born.	Suppose he writes 1953
3. Now write the number of days in a week.	He writes 7
4. Now the year he entered school.	Suppose he writes 1960
5. Now write his age.	He writes 12
6. Now write the number of years he attended school.	He writes 5
7. Tell him to add it all up.	He does, and gets 3937
8. You then produce the hidden number 3937 from your pocket or elsewhere, and he will be completely baffled.	

Note: In 1966, your number will be 3939; in 1967, it will be 3941.

How It Works

Obviously the sum of all the numbers is 3935, or in other words $2 \times 1965 + 7$. You know all this in advance because the year in which your friend was born plus his age equals 1965. The number of days in a week is always 7, and there is the answer. Be sure your friend knows the year he was born, the year he entered school, and how long he attended that school; otherwise the trick won't work.

The 2178 Trick

What You Do	*What Your Friend Does*
1. Write the number 2178 on a piece of paper; fold it and hide it.	
2. Tell your friend to write down any number between 100 and 1000. The number he writes must *not* end in 00, and the difference between the first and last digit must be greater than 1. Thus 101, 102, 536, etc. are all ruled out.	Suppose he writes 835
3. Tell him to reverse the digits and subtract the smaller number from the larger one.	He writes 538 He subtracts and gets 297
4. Now tell him to repeat this process with his new number, but add instead of subtract.	He adds 297 792 and gets 1089
5. Now tell him to multiply the result by 2.	He does, and gets 2178
6. You now produce the hidden number 2178 from your pocket or elsewhere, and he will be completely baffled.	

How It Works

This is pure algebra: $1089 = 99 \times 11$. Every three-digit number may be written as $100a + 10b + c$.

Reversing digits: $100c + 10b + \quad a$
Subtracting, we get: $100a + 10b - 100c$
$$-10b - \quad a + \quad c$$

This equals $99a - 99c$, or $99(a - c)$.

Now this $(a - c)$ equals any number from 2 to 10, thus:

$99 \times 2 = 198$	$99 \times 7 = 693$
$99 \times 3 = 297$	$99 \times 8 = 792$
$99 \times 4 = 396$	$99 \times 9 = 891$
$99 \times 5 = 495$	$99 \times 10 = 990$
$99 \times 6 = 594$	

These are the numbers that you got by reversing digits and subtracting. No matter what number you take, after reversing the digits and subtracting, you are sure to get one of the above numbers. Now if you reverse the digits and add, you will see that you always multiply 99 by 11 and get 1089. For example, $396 = 99 \times 4$, and $693 = 99 \times 7$. Add these and get 99×11, or 1089. Again, $198 = 99 \times 2$, and $891 = 99 \times 9$. Add these, and you will still get 1089. Multiplying by 2, you get 2178. Of course this works for all numbers between 100 and 1000, except the ones previously stated.

Guessing His Age

Before doing the trick, make sure you know your friend's age. Let's say that he is 12.

What You Do	*What Your Friend Does*

1. Tell your friend to take any number at all and write it down.

Suppose he writes   784

2. Now he must write the number next higher in sequence and add it to the first number.

He writes   785
He adds the two 1569

3. Now tell him to add a certain number (which you have memorized). It all depends on his age. If he is 10, he adds 19; if he is 11, he adds 21; if he is 12, he adds 23; etc. In this case he must add 23 because he is 12.

He adds 23 1,569
            23
         1,592

4. Now he must divide this by 2 and subtract the original number, and the result will be his age.

He writes 796 and subtracts the orig- 796
inal number 784 784
The answer is his age   12

How It Works

You will note that no matter what number your friend writes, if he adds the next higher number to it, the result will always be odd. In algebra, $2n + 1$ is always odd. If you now add another odd number, such as 19, 21, 23, etc., the result will be an even number; and if you divide by 2, you will get the original number again plus the number you added. When you take away the original number, what's left is the number you added, or in other words your friend's age.

The Middle Digit

This trick requires a little more care than most. You must write a large number containing an *uneven* number of digits in such a manner that all the digits *except the middle one* add up to 9 or any multiple of 9, such as 18, 27, 36, etc. Note the middle digit, write it down, and hide it. Now tell your friend to add all the digits repeatedly. When he has done this, produce the number you have hidden and he will be amazed. The middle digit must *not* be 9.

What You Do

1. Write any number with an uneven number of digits as specified above, thus:

   5628738621734

   Note that all the digits on both sides of the 8 (middle digit) add up to multiples of 9: $5 + 4$, $6 + 3$, $2 + 7$, $8 + 1$, $7 + 2$, and $3 + 6$. These all add up to 54, and if you add the middle digit you will get 62. Adding $6 + 2$, you get 8, the middle digit.

2. You have already written down the middle digit and hidden it. If you now produce it, he will be very mystified.

What Your Friend Does

He adds all these digits and gets 62, just as you did; and when he adds the last two digits he gets the middle digit, 8. He has no idea this is the middle digit, so when you produce the number 8 from your pocket he will be amazed.

How It Works

Consider a number like 435 or 46853, in which the center digit is not 9 and the sum of the remaining digits is 9 or a multiple of 9. Add all the digits, and if the sum is written with more than one digit, add the digits of the sum until only one digit remains. That remaining digit will always be the middle digit. For example:

Add the digits in 435, and you get 12. Add these two and get 3, which is the middle number in 435. Add the digits in 46853 and the result is 26. Add 2 and 6 and get 8, the middle digit. 631857254 has digits adding up to 41. Add 4 and 1 and get 5, the middle digit.

The reason for this is obvious but interesting. Each number must have an odd number of digits with a digit (not 9) in the center.

Since the sum of all digits repeatedly added is a multiple of 9, we have the simple formula $n(10 - 1) + k$, where k is the middle digit and 9 is $10 - 1$. This is $10n - n + k$; and if you add the 1 and 0 of the 10, you get $1n$ or n. Now $n - n + k = k$, the middle digit.

The Crossed-out Number

In this trick, you can tell your friend what particular digit in a four-digit number he has crossed out without seeing the number.

What You Do	*What Your Friend Does*
1. Tell your friend to write any number of four digits, and not to let you see the number.	Suppose he writes 8429
2. Now tell him to add these digits and put the result to the right.	He adds and gets 23

What You Do	*What Your Friend Does*

3. Now he must cross out one of the four digits and write the remaining three digits over the last result (the sum of the digits in the original number).

He crosses out the 8 in the original number and writes 429 over the 23

$$\begin{array}{r} 429 \\ 23 \\ \hline \end{array}$$

4. Now he must subtract one from the other.

He gets   406

5. He must now tell you his result, which is 406. As soon as you hear this, you add up the digits and subtract the sum from the next highest multiple of 9, which in this case is 18. $4 + 0 + 6 = 10$; and when you subtract 10 from 18, you get the digit he crossed out, which was 8. When you tell him this, he should be baffled.

Suppose your friend crossed out the 2 in 8429. He would then write the remaining digits 849; from this he would subtract the 23, which is the sum of all the digits in 8429. 23 from 849 is 826, and adding these digits we get 16. The next highest multiple of 9 is 18, and 16 from 18 leaves 2, which is the number he crossed out.

This trick requires a little practice, but you will soon be an expert at it. Try any other number just for practice. Take 5472 and cross out the 7. The sum of the digits is 18, and this taken from 542 leaves 524. The sum of the digits in 524 is 11; take this from 18, and you get 7—the number you crossed out. It's really very simple.

I've Got Your Number

Read this trick a few times to make sure you understand what to do, then mystify your friends with it. It is really very simple, and if you do it correctly it never fails to baffle.

What You Do	*What Your Friend Does*
1. Write down any number that is less than 99. Suppose you write 64. Fold the paper, and either hide it in your pocket or give it to your friend to hide in his pocket.	
2. Tell your friend to write down any number between 50 and 100.	Suppose he writes 72
3. Now mentally subtract the number you wrote, which was 64, from 99, and get 35. Tell your friend to add 35 to the number he wrote down.	He adds and gets 107
4. Now tell your friend to cross out the first digit and add it to the remaining digits.	He crosses out the 1 and adds it to the 07 and gets 08
5. Now tell your friend to subtract this result from the original number he wrote down.	He takes 08 from 72 and gets 64
6. At this point you unfold the paper in your pocket (or have him unfold it from his pocket) and, lo and behold, there is 64—the number you originally wrote down!	

To do this trick with higher numbers, the number you select must be between 100 and 200, while the number your friend selects can be any one between 200 and 1,000. In the third step, instead of taking your original number from 99, take it from 999.

Mathememory

MATHEMEMORY combines mathematics and memory. Do the following, and you will impress your friends with your remarkable memory and win their admiration —just as long as they don't know your secret!

An Amazing Memory

Write down a long string of numbers—the longer the better—and make sure that you always *add* the last two digits to get the next one. For example, 5 2 7 9 6 5 . . . etc. Starting with 5 2, the next digit will be 7, or 5 + 2. Then the two-digit number 16, or 7 + 9 (just put down the 6 and forget the 10 or 1). The next one will be 15, or 9 + 6 (put down the 5 and forget the 1), and so on. Here is a long string of numbers for you to examine. You can make up your own.

4 3 7 0 7 7 4 1 5 6 1 7 8 5 3 8 1 9 0 9 9 8 7 5 2 7 9 6 5...

You can see that you start with $4 + 3$ and go on from there, adding the previous two digits to get the next, and always dropping the 1 if the number comes to 10 or more. This is so simple that it is really laughable when you know about it, but it is quite startling to one who is not in the know. In doing this trick, you will have to know the first two numbers to start you off.

The Local Memory

If you happen to live in the New York area, or in any other large city that has a subway and streets that are numbered, the following trick never fails to flabbergast your friends. Just write down the local subway stops, East Side or West Side, whichever are more familiar to you. Now rattle them off, not in pairs but singly. If you say 14 18 23 etc., you will give the trick away. Instead say 1 4 1 8 2 3 2 8 etc. Here are some West Side local stops on the New York City Seventh Avenue subway:

1 4 18 23 28 33 42 50 59 66 72 79 86 96 103 110
116 125 137 145 157 168 181 191 207 215 225

The Dated Memory

This trick is a little more difficult, but at the same time it will be almost impossible to detect. For your string of numbers use dates. The first of January is, of course, 1 1. Lincoln's Birthday is 2 1 2, and the Fourth of July is 7 4. You can slip in your own birthday and the birthdays of your mother and dad, sisters and brothers (if you know these dates), and nobody will ever guess how you remember all these numbers. Suppose you were born on June 15, 1952, your mother on September 23, 1924, and your father on August 12, 1920. The string of numbers you can easily rattle off would be:

6 1 5 5 2 9 2 3 2 4 8 1 2 2 0 . . .

And if you add to these Lincoln's Birthday, the Fourth of July, Christmas, and some other famous holidays, you will completely baffle your friends.

If you examine the above numbers, you will see that June 15, 1952, is 6/15/52, September 23, 1924, is 9/23/24, and August 12, 1920 is 8/12/20. Study this system a while, and then make up your own string of digits to mystify your friends.

Family Names

This trick is very much like the preceding one, except that it is done with letters instead of numbers. Just write down the first three letters of your name and of your sisters', brothers', and friends' names. Then rattle off the letters, making sure you remember their correct order. Suppose your name is Howard and you have two sisters, Jane and Dorothy, and brother Samuel. You would then write:

H O W J A N D O R S A M . . .

and keep on adding the names of as many friends and relatives as you can think of.

To make up my own string of letters, I would write down the names of members of my family, beginning with my father (Arthur), then my mother (Jessie), my brother, (Theodore), my three sisters in order of age (Josephine, Mabel, Phyllis), and myself (Jerome), thus:

A R T J E S T H E J O S M A B P H Y J E R . . . etc.

Now you make up your own string of letters in the same way and rattle them off to the amazement of your friends.

It's Bewildering

Of all the mathememories, this trick is by far the most bewildering. You will have to practice a little before doing it, yet it is really just as simple as the first trick in this series. In the table on page 15, you will see two-digit numbers in boldface type, and under each such number a long series of digits. Under the boldface number 14, for example, you will see the digits 7291011235831; under number 21, the digits 4370774156178. Show this table to a friend and ask him to select any boldface number, tell it to you, and you will give him the large number directly under it. As soon as he does this, you add 13 and *reverse the digits*. Then proceed as instructed in the first mathememory on page 11.

Suppose he selects 14. You add 13 and get 27. Now reverse the digits and proceed as shown, adding the previous two digits to get the next one, until you have the given number: 7291011235831. It is as simple as all that, but be sure to give *only* thirteen digits and no more; otherwise you may give the trick away.

MATHEMEMORY TABLE

14	21	18
7291011235831	4370774156178	1347189763921

23	15	26
6392134718976	8202246066280	9325729101123

41	33	29
4594370774156	6404482022460	2460662808864

32	24	12
5493257291011	7303369549325	5279651673033

Some Interesting Numbers

No Repeating Digits

How MANY LONG WORDS do you know that have no repeating letters? *Dumbwaiter, playground, Republican,* and *workmanship* are a few such words. If you examine them, you will see that each letter appears once and only once.

Rare as such words are, it is even rarer to find an eight-digit number in which no digit is repeated, and much more so to find such a number which, when multiplied by 9, gives a nine-digit number in which no digit is repeated. Take any eight-digit number at random, multiply it by 9, and you are sure to get a repetition of digits. For example:

$$65298741 \times 9 = 587688669$$
$$17254986 \times 9 = 155294874$$

You can go on and on, and you will nearly always get a product with repeating digits. Yet it so happens that a brilliant and unknown mathematician has found four eight-digit numbers with no repeating digits, each of which, when multiplied by 9, gives a nine-digit number with no repetitions. Here they are:

$$81274365 \times 9 = 731469285$$
$$72645831 \times 9 = 653812479$$
$$58132764 \times 9 = 523194876$$
$$76125484 \times 9 = 685129347$$

Not only that, but when each of these four numbers is multiplied by 18, the result is a ten-digit number with no repeating digits:

$$81274365 \times 18 = 1462938570$$
$$72645831 \times 18 = 1307624958$$
$$58132764 \times 18 = 1046389752$$
$$76125483 \times 18 = 1370258694$$

Note that there is no 9 in any of these eight-digit numbers.

It would be indeed interesting for you to look for other eight-digit numbers with no repeating digits and no 9 which have the same properties as the four numbers given here. The chances of your finding such a number is as rare as dealing a hand of thirteen spades from a shuffled pack of cards. But go ahead and try!

Casting Out Nines

If you want to see whether or not a sum of numbers is correct, all you need to do is add the digits in each row and add the digits in the sum. If the results agree, the sum of all the numbers is correct. For example:

Is this addition correct?

$$
\begin{array}{r}
18964 \\
21478 \\
54298 \\
14376 \\
\hline
138472
\end{array}
$$

To check, add each row thus:

$$1+8+9+6+4=28 \qquad 2+8=10=1$$
$$2+1+4+7+8=22 \qquad 2+2=4=4$$
$$5+4+2+9+8=28 \qquad 2+8=10=1$$
$$1+4+3+7+6=21 \qquad 2+1=3=3$$
$$\overline{9}$$

$$1+3+8+4+7+2=25 \qquad 2+5=7$$

Since 7 and 9 do not agree, the addition is not correct.

Here is another one for practice:

Is this addition correct?

$$
\begin{array}{r}
2567432 \\
3749816 \\
5625439 \\
6735418 \\
\hline
18678105
\end{array}
$$

To check, add each row thus:

$$2+5+6+7+4+3+2=29 \quad 2+9=11=\ 2$$
$$3+7+4+9+8+1+6=38 \quad 3+8=11=\ 2$$
$$5+6+2+5+4+3+9=34 \quad 3+4=\ 7=\ 7$$
$$6+7+3+5+4+1+8=34 \quad 3+4=\ 7=\ 7$$
$$\overline{18}$$

$$1+8=9$$
$$1+8+6+7+8+1+0+5=36 \qquad 3+6=9$$

Since 9 agrees with 9, the addition is correct.

To repeat: in any addition, just add the digits in each row and get the sum of these added digits. Then add the digits of the sum of all the numbers, and if the two agree the addition is correct; if they do not agree, the addition is *not* correct. Just for practice, are the following additions correct or wrong?

89635	8563752
56234	5735749
89725	1184672
44871	1256389
280465	5568051
	22308613

To check subtraction, use the same method as for addition, except that you subtract one number from the other. For example:

Is this subtraction correct?

$$978494238$$
$$163865306$$
$$\overline{814628932}$$

$$9+7+8+4+9+4+2+3+8=54 \qquad 5+4=9$$
$$1+6+3+8+6+5+3+0+6=38 \qquad 3+8=11$$
$$\underline{1+1=2}$$
$$9-2=7$$
$$8+1+4+6+2+8+9+3+2=43 \qquad 4+3=7$$

Since the two 7's agree, the subtraction is correct.

To check multiplication, we multiply instead of add at first. Then we add the digits in the result.
For example:

Is this multiplication correct?

$$
\begin{array}{r}
14963 = 23 = 5 \\
371 = 11 = 2 \\
\hline
14963 \qquad \overline{10}\,(2 \times 5) = 1 \\
104741 \\
44889 \\
\hline
\overline{5551273} = 28 = 10 - 1
\end{array}
$$

The digits agree, so the multiplication is correct.

Is this multiplication correct?

$$
\begin{array}{r}
15729 = 24 = 6 \\
412 = 9 = 9 \\
\hline
31458 \qquad \overline{54}\,(9 \times 6) \\
15729 \qquad\qquad 5 + 4 = 9 \\
64914 \\
\hline
\overline{6680048} = 32 = 5
\end{array}
$$

The digits do not agree, so the multiplication is wrong.

The Personalities of Numbers

Numbers have personalities just like people. Just as some people are witty and lively, and others are dull and tiresome, so some numbers are extremely interesting and others are commonplace. Of course you are well acquainted with *square numbers,* such as 1, 4, 9, 16, 25, etc. These are the squares of 1, 2, 3, 4, 5, etc. and can be represented by dots in a square, as shown in Figure 1.

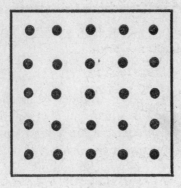

FIGURE 1

Now there are also *triangular numbers,* such as 1, 3, 6, 10, 15, 21, 28, etc. Notice that each number is found by adding progressive numbers to the previous number; thus we add 2 to 1 and get 3, 3 to 3 and get 6, 4 to 6 and get 10, 5 to 10 and get 15, 6 to 15 and get 21, and so on. These numbers can be represented by dots in the form of a triangle, as shown in Figure 2 on page 22.

FIGURE 2

If you examine Figure 3, you will see how triangular numbers are related to square numbers, and how all consecutive uneven numbers, when added up, form square numbers. A little study of the chart will reveal some very interesting things. In the first column we have the triangular numbers, in the second column the square numbers, and in the third column the uneven numbers. Note that the first two triangular numbers, 1 and 3, add up to 4—a square number. The next two triangular numbers add up to 9, the next square number—and so on for each successive pair of triangular numbers. Note also that adding the first *two* uneven numbers gives the square of 2, adding the first *three* uneven numbers gives the square of 3, and so on. Note, too, that when you subtract a triangular number from a succeeding square number, you get the next triangular number; thus 3 from 9 = 6, 6 from 16 = 10, 10 from 25 = 15, etc. See how many more interesting things you can find out from this amazing chart.

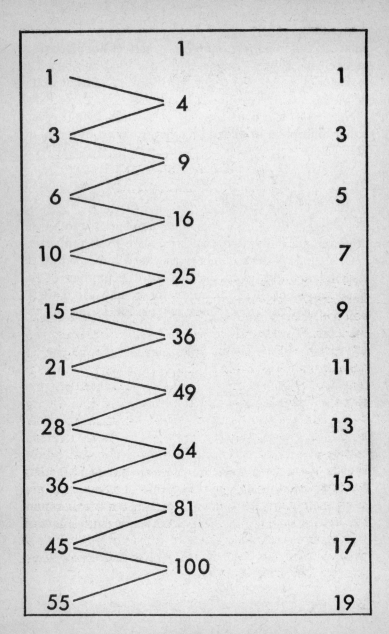

FIGURE 3

In addition to triangular and square numbers, we have what are called *perfect numbers*. A perfect number is any number all of whose factors add up to that number. The most perfect number is 6—indeed, if it were a girl, it would be the Miss Universe of all the numbers.

Numbers 4 and 6 are the only ones whose factors, when either multiplied or added together, total up to the number. Thus:

$$2 \times 2 = 4 \quad \text{and} \quad 2 + 2 = 4$$
$$1 \times 2 \times 3 = 6 \quad \text{and} \quad 1 + 2 + 3 = 6$$

The number 6 is also a triangular number. There are no other numbers anywhere that have all of these properties.

Of course perfect numbers are very rare, and while their factors add up to the number, the product of the factors does not. This is true only for 4 and 6. Here are six perfect numbers; room does not permit listing all the factors:

$$6 = 1 + 2 + 3$$
$$28 = 1 + 2 + 4 + 7 + 14$$
$$496 =$$
$$8128 =$$
$$33550336 =$$
$$8589869056 =$$

The general formula for perfect numbers is $2^{p-1}(2^p - 1)$, where p and $2^p - 1$ are prime numbers.

You can see that it is quite a mathematical task to hunt up and test perfect numbers. Some mathematicians have worked out perfect numbers up to 18 places. The result has 750 digits and would be about 15 feet long if written out in type this size. That number of bacteria would overflow the Milky Way galaxy!

Perfect numbers are more interesting than they are practical, but two of them stand out above all the others: 6 and 28. We have already described the properties of 6, and 28 is the only other number that is both perfect and triangular.

Beautiful Number Arrangements

I F YOU WRITE THE NUMBER 037037037037 and multiply it
by 3, 6, 9, 12, 15, etc., you get numbers consisting of
all 1's, all 2's, all 3's, etc., thus:

$$
\begin{aligned}
037037037037 \times\ \ 3 &= 111111111111 \\
\times\ \ 6 &= 222222222222 \\
\times\ \ 9 &= 333333333333 \\
\times 12 &= 444444444444 \\
\times 15 &= 555555555555 \\
\times 18 &= 666666666666 \\
\times 21 &= 777777777777 \\
\times 24 &= 888888888888 \\
\times 28 &= 999999999999 \\
\times 30 &= 1000000000000
\end{aligned}
$$

Here are some pretty number arrangements. Many of them were created by the late Royal V. Heath, in his book *Mathemagic*, published by Dover Publications.

$$1 + 2 = 3$$
$$4 + 5 + 6 = 7 + 8$$
$$9 + 10 + 11 + 12 = 13 + 14 + 15$$
$$16 + 17 + 18 + 19 + 20 = 21 + 22 + 23 + 24$$

. . . .

In the following, the denominator of the fraction has the same digits as the whole number with plus signs between:

$$121 = \frac{22 \times 22}{1 + 2 + 1} = \frac{484}{2} = 121$$

$$12321 = \frac{333 \times 333}{1 + 2 + 3 + 2 + 1} = \frac{110889}{9} = 12321$$

$$1234321 = \frac{4444 \times 4444}{1 + 2 + 3 + 4 + 3 + 2 + 1} = \frac{1974136}{16} = 1234321$$

The next number will be five 5's times five 5's divided by 25 (the square of 5), which gives 123454321. The center digit in each whole number sets the pace. If it is n, for example, the numerator will be n n's times n n's, and the denominator will be n^2, in order to bring back the original number.

The magic number 076923, when multiplied by 1, 10, 9, 12, 3, and 4 respectively, not only keeps on repeating the digits, but it also reads 076923 vertically, thus:

$$076923 \times \quad 1 = 076923$$
$$\times 10 = 769230$$
$$\times \quad 9 = 692307$$
$$\times 12 = 923076$$
$$\times \quad 3 = 230769$$
$$\times \quad 4 = 307692$$

Note that the first column of numbers after the equal sign reads 076923 vertically, and that all the other columns have the same sequence of digits as do the rows.

If this magic number is now multiplied by 2, 7, 5, 11, 6, and 8 respectively, we get a new number, 153846, which is twice 076923 and has the same properties, thus:

$$76923 \times \quad 2 = 153846$$
$$\times \quad 7 = 538461$$
$$\times \quad 5 = 384615$$
$$\times 11 = 846153$$
$$\times \quad 6 = 461538$$
$$\times \quad 8 = 615384$$

Note that the sum of the digits in each row and column in all these numbers add up to 27.

Here are two other pretty number arrangements:

$$0 \times 9 + 8 = 8$$
$$9 \times 9 + 7 = 88$$
$$98 \times 9 + 6 = 888$$
$$987 \times 9 + 5 = 8888$$
$$9876 \times 9 + 4 = 88888$$
$$98765 \times 9 + 3 = 888888$$
$$987654 \times 9 + 2 = 8888888$$
$$9876543 \times 9 + 1 = 88888888$$

$$1 \times 8 + 1 = 9$$
$$12 \times 8 + 2 = 98$$
$$123 \times 8 + 3 = 987$$
$$1234 \times 8 + 4 = 9876$$
$$12345 \times 8 + 5 = 98765$$
$$123456 \times 8 + 6 = 987654$$
$$1234567 \times 8 + 7 = 9876543$$
$$12345678 \times 8 + 8 = 98765432$$
$$123456789 \times 8 + 9 = 987654321$$

The Fascination of Numbers

A Peculiar Way to Multiply

I ONCE KNEW A MAN who never learned to multiply or work with fractions. All he could do was multiply and divide by 2—nothing more. Yet he always got the correct answer in any multiplication problem. When asked to multiply 54 by 67, for example, he went about it as follows:

$$
\begin{array}{r}
54 \times 67 \\
27 \times 134 \\
13 \times 268 \\
6 \times 536 \\
3 \times 1072 \\
1 \times 2144 \\
\end{array}
$$

You will see that he always divided the numbers in the first column by 2, and multiplied those in the second column by 2. When told that half of 27 is 13½ and half of

13 is 6½, he said he knew nothing about fractions—they annoyed him. He crossed out all even numbers in the first column, going all the way through column 2, then added the remaining numbers in column 2, thus:

$$
\begin{array}{r}
\cancel{54 \times \quad 67} \\
27 \times \quad 134 \\
13 \times \quad 268 \\
\cancel{6 \times \quad 536} \\
3 \times 1072 \\
1 \times 2144 \\
\hline
3618
\end{array}
$$

Check: $54 \times 67 = 3618$

Try another:

$$
\begin{array}{r}
15 \times \quad 47 \\
7 \times \quad 94 \\
3 \times 188 \\
1 \times 376 \\
\hline
705
\end{array}
$$

Check: $15 \times 47 = 705$

$$
\begin{array}{r}
29 \times \quad 17 \\
\cancel{14 \times \quad 34} \\
7 \times \quad 68 \\
3 \times 136 \\
1 \times 272 \\
\hline
493
\end{array}
$$

Check: $29 \times 17 = 493$

Lightning Multiplication

The reciprocals of certain prime numbers have some very interesting properties. The number 7 is a prime number, and its reciprocal is 1/7. When written in decimal form, the reciprocal is 142857142857142857. . . . If you examine this number, you will see that 142857 keeps on repeating over and over again. To multiply this number by any number less than 4, all you need to do is mentally to multiply the first two digits by the number and run the number through. By "running the number through" we mean copying all the digits in order, for their order never changes.

To multiply by 2, you see that $2 \times 14 = 28$, so you begin with 28 and run the number through. To multiply by 3, begin with 42 $(3 \times 14 = 42)$ and follow through. To multiply by 4, 5, and 6, you do the same except that you add 1 to the product of the first two digits. Thus:

$$142857 \times 2 = 285714 \qquad 142857 \times 5 = 714285$$
$$142857 \times 3 = 428571 \qquad 142857 \times 6 = 857142$$
$$142857 \times 4 = 571428 \qquad 142857 \times 7 = 999999$$

Once you have mastered this principle of starting at a certain point in this number and copying all the digits in their regular order until they repeat, try a more complicated number, such as the reciprocal of 17, which is 1/17 or 5882352941176470588235294117647058823529411764 70 . . .

This is a much larger number, and you will note that it repeats itself after the first sixteen digits, which are 5882352941176470. You can treat this number the same as the 142857 shown above, and it will be much more baffling to your audience. To multiply this larger number by any number less than 17, consider the first two digits, 58, as a little less than 60; or if you say 5.8, it will be a little less than 6. To multiply the number by 4, for example, say to yourself: "4 × 6 = 24. It starts at a little less than 24, so I'll begin at 23 and run the number through for the sixteen digits." To multiply the number by 2, say to yourself: "2 × 6 = 12. It starts at a little less than 12, so I'll begin at 11 and run the number through."

Here are more examples:

5882352941176470 × 2 = 11764705882352950
2 × 6 = 12,   so start at 11.

5882352941176470 × 3 = 17647058823529410
3 × 6 = 18,   so start at 17.

5882352941176470 × 4 = 23529411764705880
4 × 6 = 24,   so start at 23.

5882352941176470 × 5 = 29411764705882350
5 × 6 = 30,   so start at 29.

5882352941176470 × 6 = 35294117647058820
6 × 6 = 36,   so start at 35.

You can see that the principle is very simple. It is just a question of starting off with the correct two digits and copying all the rest of the digits in their regular order.

Lightning Magic Calculations

Ask a friend to select any number from the table below. All he needs to do is tell you in which columns the selected number appears, and you will tell him what number it is. Suppose he selects 20 and tells you it appears in Columns III and V, which it does. Then all you do is *add* the first numbers of Columns III and V. In Column III you find 4, and in Column V you find 16. $16 + 4 = 20$, which is his number.

Suppose he selects 15 and tells you his number appears in Columns I, II, III, and IV. Then all you do is add the first four numbers in these columns: $1 + 2 + 4 + 8 = 15$, and you have found his number.

Practice a little before you spring this trick.

I	II	III	IV	V
1	2	4	8	16
11	18	5	13	24
9	11	14	11	18
5	14	13	24	22
13	7	7	10	17
17	10	22	14	19
3	22	6	15	20
19	3	28	26	23
15	6	20	27	26
23	19	15	28	27
27	15	23	31	28
31	23	31	12	30
21	26	30	30	31
25	27	29	29	29
29	31	25	9	21
7	30	12	25	25

Multiplication and addition seem to be related when you consider the following:

$$1 + \tfrac{1}{2} \times 3 = 4\tfrac{1}{2} \qquad 1 + \tfrac{1}{2} + 3 = 4\tfrac{1}{2}$$
$$1 + \tfrac{1}{3} \times 4 = 5\tfrac{1}{3} \qquad 1 + \tfrac{1}{3} + 4 = 5\tfrac{1}{3}$$
$$1 + \tfrac{1}{4} \times 5 = 6\tfrac{1}{4} \qquad 1 + \tfrac{1}{4} + 5 = 6\tfrac{1}{4}$$

In general:

$$1 + 1/n \times (n+1) = 1 + 1/n + (n+1)$$

Note also these relationships:

Multiplication and Subtraction

$$1 \times \tfrac{1}{2} = 1 - \tfrac{1}{2} = \tfrac{1}{2}$$
$$2 \times \tfrac{2}{3} = 2 - \tfrac{2}{3} = 1\tfrac{1}{3}$$
$$3 \times \tfrac{3}{4} = 3 - \tfrac{3}{4} = 2\tfrac{1}{4}$$
$$4 \times \tfrac{4}{5} = 4 - \tfrac{4}{5} = 3\tfrac{1}{5}$$
$$5 \times \tfrac{5}{6} = 5 - \tfrac{5}{6} = 4\tfrac{1}{6}$$

$$n \times \frac{n}{n+1} = n - \frac{n}{n+1}$$

Division and Addition

$$1\tfrac{1}{3} \div \tfrac{2}{3} = 1\tfrac{1}{3} + \tfrac{2}{3} = 2$$
$$2\tfrac{1}{4} \div \tfrac{3}{4} = 2\tfrac{1}{4} + \tfrac{3}{4} = 3$$
$$3\tfrac{1}{5} \div \tfrac{4}{5} = 3\tfrac{1}{5} + \tfrac{4}{5} = 4$$
$$4\tfrac{1}{6} \div \tfrac{5}{6} = 4\tfrac{1}{6} + \tfrac{5}{6} = 5$$

$$\left(n + \frac{1}{n+2}\right) \div \frac{n+1}{n+2} = \left(n + \frac{1}{n+2}\right) + \frac{n+1}{n+2}$$

Division and Subtraction

$$4\frac{1}{2} \div 3 = 4\frac{1}{2} - 3 = 1\frac{1}{2}$$
$$5\frac{1}{3} \div 4 = 5\frac{1}{3} - 4 = 1\frac{1}{3}$$
$$6\frac{1}{4} \div 5 = 6\frac{1}{4} - 5 = 1\frac{1}{4}$$
$$7\frac{1}{5} \div 6 = 7\frac{1}{5} - 6 = 1\frac{1}{5}$$

$$n + \left(\frac{1}{n-2}\right) \div (n-1) = n + \left(\frac{1}{n-2}\right) - (n-1)$$

One-second Addition

In precisely one second, you can add five three-digit numbers, as given in the table below—much to the amazement of your friends. Just ask someone to write down a number from each of the five columns in this table. As soon as he does, you add the five *last* digits mentally, subtract this sum from 50, and tack it on to the result.

I	II	III	IV	V
69	345	186	872	756
366	642	582	278	558
168	246	87	575	657
762	147	285	377	954
663	543	483	179	855
564	48	384	674	459

For example, suppose your friend selects 168, 543, 285, 674, and 756. All you do is add 8, 3, 5, 4, and 6 mentally and get 26. Take this from 50, and you get 24. Tack this 24 on to the 26 and get 2426, which is the answer. Meanwhile your friend checks your one-second addition by adding:

$$
\begin{array}{r}
168 \\
543 \\
285 \\
674 \\
756 \\
\hline
2426
\end{array}
$$

It will take him fifteen or twenty seconds to check your answer.

Suppose your friend chooses 69, 147, 582, 377, and 459. You add 9, 7, 2, 7, and 9 mentally and get 34. Subtract 34 from 50, and you get 16. The answer is 1634, which he can check after fifteen or twenty seconds by the long method:

$$
\begin{array}{r}
69 \\
147 \\
582 \\
377 \\
459 \\
\hline
1634
\end{array}
$$

Of course your friend must always tell you the numbers he selects from each column, and by this magic system you can add them in one second flat and amaze him.

A Remarkable Date Chart

The date chart shown in Figure 4 is by Mr. Harry D. Ruderman, a brilliant mathematician. To find on what day a certain date will fall, connect the month on the month line (right) with the date on the date line (left) and note where it crosses the center line. The chart is set for 1964, which happens to be leap year. This means that, after the month of February, you must *add a day* to the one shown on the center line.

For example, on what day will the Fourth of July fall in 1964? Connect *July*, the bottom month on the right, with *4* (the middle date on the left) and you will see that the line crosses *Friday*. Now because this is leap year, add a day, and the answer is *Saturday*.

On what day will Christmas fall in 1964? Connect *December* with 25 and get *Thursday*. Because this is leap year, add a day, and the answer is *Friday*.

Note that you add a day only when it is leap year and the month follows February. Washington's Birthday in 1964 falls on a Saturday, so you connect *February* with 22 and get *Saturday*. Since the month is not later than February, there is no need to add a day.

The strip, Figure 5, gives the days of the week for the next five years. Make a copy and place it on the center line of Figure 4, making sure that the year is on the first line. For example, on what day will April 21 fall in 1967? Move the strip so that 1967 (Sunday) comes on the top line. Now proceed as before and get *Friday*. It's as simple as all that. After you have practiced a while, you will be able to tell quickly and accurately on what day any date up to December 31, 1969, will fall. Remember that 1968 is another leap year, so add a day after the month of February.

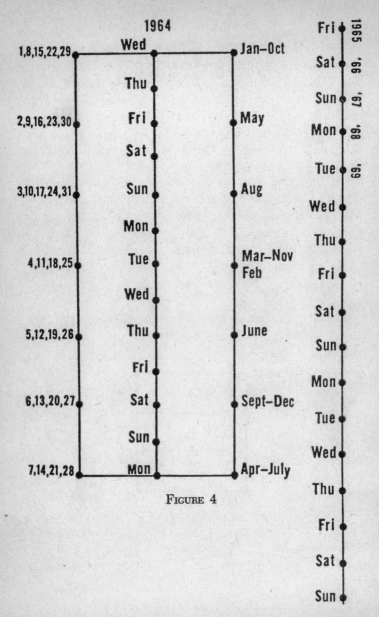

FIGURE 4

FIGURE 5

Magic Squares*

M AGIC SQUARES were discovered by the Egyptians a few thousand years ago, so they are very old indeed. They were originally dedicated to the then known seven planets, although nobody knows just why. The whole idea of a magic square is to arrange numbers in boxes in a square so that all lines, columns, and diagonals all add up to the same number.

The Three-cell Magic Square

The simplest magic square, of course, is one containing only nine boxes, with numbers from 1 to 9 inclusive, as shown in Figure 6.

8	1	6
3	5	7
4	9	2

15

FIGURE 6

---

* Adapted from *Mathemagic*, by Royal V. Heath, Dover Publications, 1953.

You will see that each row and each column adds up to 15. Also, the two diagonals add up to 15.

The Four-cell Magic Square

The next type of magic square is the four-cell square, in which all the numbers add up to 34. This is far more interesting than the three-cell square. If you study Figure 7 carefully, you will discover some amazing facts.

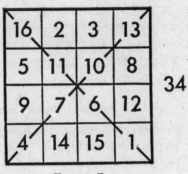

FIGURE 7

Not only does every row and column add up to 34, but the four corner squares—16, 13, 1, and 4—as well as the two middle top and bottom squares—3, 2, 15, and 14—and the two center left and right squares—5, 9, 8, and 12—all add up to 34.

There are so many ways of making 34 with this amazing magic square that we have provided a square that has letters instead of numbers, Figure 8, so that you can translate the letters into corresponding numbers given in the magic square. Thus A corresponds to 16, B to 3, C to 2, and so on.

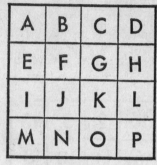

FIGURE 8

You can now see that:

$$
\begin{array}{rcccccccl}
B & + & C & + & N & + & O & = & 34 \\
E & + & I & + & H & + & L & = & 34 \\
A & + & D & + & P & + & M & = & 34 \\
F & + & G & + & J & + & K & = & 34 \\
I & + & N & + & C & + & H & = & 34 \\
E & + & B & + & L & + & O & = & 34 \\
A & + & F & + & K & + & P & = & 34 \\
D & + & G & + & J & + & M & = & 34 \\
\end{array}
$$

Note also that every column as well as every row in the magic square adds up to 34.

But this is only the beginning. The sum of the squares of the numbers in the first and third rows equals the sum

42

of the squares of the numbers in the second and fourth rows, thus:

$$16^2 + 3^2 + 2^2 + 13^2 + 9^2 + 6^2 + 7^2 + 12^2 = 748$$
$$5^2 + 10^2 + 11^2 + 8^2 + 4^2 + 15^2 + 14^2 + 1^2 = 748$$

And, believe it or not, the same is true for the vertical columns. The sum of the squares of the numbers in the first and third columns equals the sum of the squares of the numbers in the second and last columns, thus:

16^2	3^2
5^2	10^2
9^2	6^2
4^2	15^2
2^2	13^2
11^2	8^2
7^2	12^2
14^2	1^2
$\overline{748}$	$\overline{748}$

Moreover, the sum of the squares of all the numbers in the first two columns equals the sum of the squares of all the numbers in the last two columns. The same applies to the first and last two rows. This is truly an amazing square.

Of course a magic square as remarkable as this is very well known. It first appeared in the famous painting by the great German artist, Albrecht Dürer, in the year 1514—a date which is clearly shown at the bottom of the square itself, adding more mystery to it. The painting, which is called "Melancholia," depicts a number of scientific instruments.

The Upside-down Magic Square

Another remarkable magic square, created by the late Royal V. Heath and fully described in my book *Fun with Mathematics,* is shown here. The numbers in this square make 264 in forty-eight different ways. Not only do all rows, columns, diagonals, center squares, edge squares, and other combinations add up to 264, just as they added up to 34 in the previous magic square, but the same thing happens if you turn the square *upside down!*

96	11	89	68
88	69	91	16
61	86	18	99
19	98	66	81

264

FIGURE 9

This is perhaps the most amazing of all the magic squares. It goes the "Melancholia" magic square one better, for it does the same things upside down that it does right side up.

How to Make Magic Squares

There are two methods of making magic squares. One applies to uneven-cell squares—3, 5, 7, etc.—and the other to even-cell squares—4, 8, 12, etc. To make an uneven-cell magic square, we use the *diagonal-arrow method;* to make an even-cell square, we use the *cross-diagonal method.* These methods are described as follows.

Uneven-cell Magic Squares

To make an uneven-cell square of three cells, for example, place number 1 in the top center square and proceed slantingly up to the right (see arrow) at 45 degrees. The next number will be 2, but it is up to the right and off the main square, so it goes in the corresponding position below in the last row. The next number is 3, which is also up to the right and off the main square, so it goes in the corresponding position to the left in the center of the first

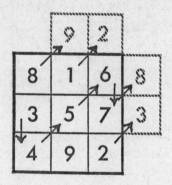

Figure 10

45

column. The next number, 4, can't go slantingly up to the right because the 1 is in the way, so we drop down one square and then go 4, 5, and 6 along the diagonal of the main square. Now we drop down one square and place 7 under the 6, putting 8 and 9 in their positions according to the main rule. Thus placing the *next number slantingly up to the right* is the rule for constructing all uneven-cell magic squares. You can see from the five-cell magic square below that the same procedure applies.

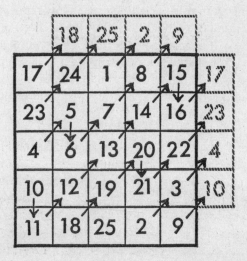

FIGURE 11

Even-cell Magic Squares

To make an even-cell magic square of four cells, for example, first draw the two diagonals lightly in pencil and, starting with *last* number—16, or 4^2—count backward, as shown below:

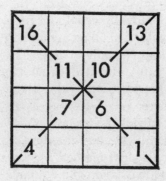

FIGURE 12

Wherever the lightly penciled diagonal crosses a cell, a number is required. Start by putting the last number, 16, in the very first cell. Now, working across, skip two cells, since there are no pencil lines in them, and count backward to yourself 15, 14; then put 13 in the other corner cell with the pencil line in it. Now start with the next row, down. There is no line in the first cell, so skip it, counting 12 to yourself; and put 11 and 10 in the next two cells which have the diagonal lines in them. Skip the last cell in that row and the first cell in the third row, counting to yourself

47

9, 8, and put 7 and 6 in the two center cells because the diagonal crosses them. The last cell in that row is skipped (it would be 5 if a diagonal), and the last row of course is 4 . . 1. You now have a half-filled square, so you start all over again, filling in the blanks with the missing numbers progressively, thus: 2, 3, 5, 8, 9, 12, 14, 15. If you do this correctly, you will have the famous magic square we have already discussed (see page 41).

The diagonal method of filling in numbers to make even-cell magic squares applies only to squares having a multiple of four cells: 4, 8, 12, etc. It does not apply to squares having six, ten, fourteen, etc. cells; these are too complicated to give here.

In making all magic squares, you must use these two methods: the slantingly-up-to-the-right for *uneven*-cell squares and the diagonal method for *even*-cell that are multiples of 4. You may begin at any number other than 1 if you wish, but you must progress consecutively and not omit any numbers. Two magic squares starting with numbers other than 1 are shown, and you will see the system is the same as before.

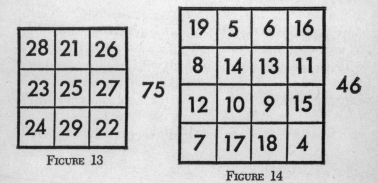

FIGURE 13   FIGURE 14

48

What Numbers Will Magic Squares Add Up to?

We have seen that a magic square of three cells has all rows and columns adding up to 15 when numbers from 1 to 9 are used. We have seen that a magic square of four cells has rows and columns adding up to 34 when all numbers from 1 to 16 are used. What about a five-, six-, or seven-cell, or larger, magic square? What will the rows and columns of these add up to? There is a formula for this and it goes: cube the number of cells in the row and add the result to itself. Now divide by 2, and that is your answer. If n is the number of cells, then the rows and columns add up to $\dfrac{n^3 + n}{2}$, provided we start with 1.

Following this through, we have:

In a three-cell square, $n = 3$:

$$\frac{n^3 + n}{2} = \frac{27 + 3}{2} = 15$$

All rows and columns add up to 15.

In a four-cell square, $n = 4$:

$$\frac{n^3 + n}{2} = \frac{64 + 4}{2} = 34$$

All rows and columns add up to 34.

In a five-cell square, $n = 5$:

$$\frac{n^3 + n}{2} = \frac{125 + 5}{2} = 65$$

All rows and columns add up to 65.

In a six-cell square, $n = 6$:

$$\frac{n^3 + n}{2} = \frac{216 + 6}{2} = 111$$

All rows and columns add up to 111.

In a seven-cell square, $n = 7$:

$$\frac{n^3 + n}{2} = \frac{243 + 7}{2} = 125$$

All rows and columns add up to 125.

How to Be a Magic-square Magician

Ask a friend to mention any number between 5 and 25, and say you will put it into a magic square and tell him what every row and column will add up to before doing it. It is best to do this trick with a three-cell square first. The formula is extremely simple. It is $3n + 12$, where n is the number of cells (in this case three).

Suppose your friend gives you the number 8. Right away you mentally multiply this by 3 and add 12, and get 36 ($3 \times 8 = 24 + 12 = 36$). You then tell him that all the rows and columns in the magic square starting with his number 8 will add up to 36. Now make a magic square of three cells, putting 8 in the middle top cell, thus:

15	8	13
10	12	14
11	16	9

36

FIGURE 15

50

You can see that every row and column, as well as the diagonals, add up to 36.

If your friend had chosen 17 instead of 8, you mentally multiply 17 by 3 and add 12 to get 63 ($3 \times 17 = 51 + 12 = 63$), and tell your friend that every row and column will add up to 63 with the number he has given you. Now make the magic square with 17 in the middle top cell, thus:

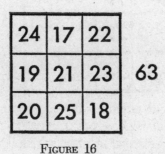

FIGURE 16

You can see that every row and column as well as the two diagonals add up to 63. This system works for any other number.

If you wish to try a four-cell magic square, all you need do is multiply the number he gives you by 4, and every row and column and the two diagonals of the new four-cell magic square will add up to that number. Your friend, however, must choose any number between 20 and 45. Suppose he chooses 21. Multiplying this by 4, you get 84, so every row and column and the two diagonals will add up to 84. The four-cell magic square must be made the way you were shown on page 47. Use the two diagonals and begin with his number 21. When you start filling in the blanks, go progressively up instead of down, so the cell next to the 21 will be 22, then 23, etc. You will see that all rows and columns in this magic square add up to 84—the number you announced to your friend before making the square as follows:

21	22	23	18
25	16	15	28
29	12	11	32
9	34	35	6

84

FIGURE 17

If your friend chooses 37, you can tell him every row and column and the two diagonals will add up to 148. After you have made the magic square starting with his number 37, let him verify the number 148. He will be amazed.

37	38	39	34
41	32	31	44
45	28	27	48
25	50	51	22

148

FIGURE 18

There are thousands of different magic squares, some of which are extremely complicated and difficult to create (such as those shown in the *Encyclopaedia Britannica*), while others are very simple. Magic squares are useful as curiosities, but have little practical value. They are the mathematical equivalent of the word puzzle, which originated a hundred years ago and eventually became the famous crossword puzzle of today. Here, for example, is a magic-square word puzzle in which the letters spell five different words vertically and horizontally, as well as backward and forward:

No matter how you read these five words—across, up and down, backward, bottom to top—they will always spell the same. This is just what a magic square does with numbers.

In conclusion, we give here a rare *multiplication* magic square which makes 120 in both directions:

$$1 \quad \cdot \quad 12 \quad \cdot \quad 10$$
$$15 \quad \cdot \quad 2 \quad \cdot \quad 4$$
$$8 \quad \cdot \quad 5 \quad \cdot \quad 3$$

There Seems to Be Something Wrong

HERE ARE a few apparent fallacies in mathematical reasoning. In how many of the following "proofs," can you find what is wrong? The answers are given on page 57.

1. *When 64 = 65.* This fallacy is not new. It has appeared in many mathematics books, and is something to think about if you have never seen it before. Figure 19 shows sixty-four small squares in the large square, which measures 8 by 8 units. Now you can see that this 8-by-8-unit square can be cut up and rearranged to form an oblong or rectangle whose sides are 13 and 5, respectively. But this new area is sixty-five squares. Apparently, in transforming one figure into the other, we gained a square. How is this possible?

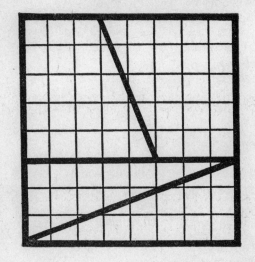

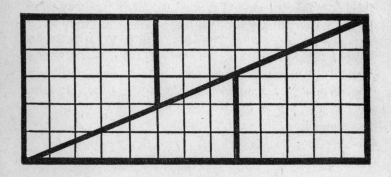

FIGURE 19

2. When $1 = 2$:

Let $a = b$
Then $ab = b^2$
Then $ab - a^2 = b^2 - a^2$
Factoring, we get $a(b-a) = (b+a)(b-a)$
Dividing out this $(b-a)$, we get $a = b + a$
But $b = a$
Hence $a = 2a$, or $1 = 2$

What is wrong here?

3. When $4 = 8$:

$16 - 48 = 64 - 96$ (both sides equal -32)
Adding 36 to both sides, $16 - 48 + 36 = 64 - 96 + 36$
Then $(4-6)^2 = (8-6)^2$
Taking the square roots, we get $4 - 6 = 8 - 6$
Hence $4 = 8$

What is wrong here?

4. When $6 \times 0 = 6$. If I add nothing to 6, it is still 6 since I didn't add anything to it. If I take nothing away from 6, it is still 6 since I didn't take anything away from it. If I now multiply 6 by nothing, I don't multiply it by anything, so it is still 6. Thus $6 \times 0 = 6$. What is wrong here?

5. *A dog has nine legs, and a ham sandwich is better than complete happiness.*

Answers

1. If you work very carefully, you will see that the rectangle does not make two perfect right triangles. Their hypotenuse will not be an exactly straight line, as it should be, but will be bent just enough to account for the extra square.

2. $a - b = 0$, and division by 0 is ruled out of mathematics.

3. $(4 - 6)^2$ has two roots: $4 - 6$ and $-4 + 6$. Similarly, $(8 - 6)^2$ has two roots: $8 - 6$ and $-8 + 6$. This gives the following true equations:

$$4 - 6 = -8 + 6$$
$$-4 + 6 = 8 - 6$$

4. Multiplication is really continued addition. If you multiply 3 by 6, you are really *adding* three 6's together. Instead of going to the trouble of adding 72 forty-five times when we multiply 45 by 72, we use the process of multiplication. Similarly, if you multiply 6 by zero, it means that you are adding zero six times, and the sum of six zeros is still zero—not 6.

5. No dog has five legs, but any dog has four legs more than no dog; hence a dog has nine legs. Nothing is better than complete happiness, and a ham sandwich is certainly better than nothing.

How to Make a Slide Rule
from an Ordinary Ruler*

UNDOUBTEDLY you have seen or used a slide rule at some
time or other, and you know it consists of a rule
with a slide in it, as shown on page 59. By moving the slide
back and forth, you can multiply and divide numbers
very quickly, as well as do proportion, take square and
cube roots, and raise to those powers. In one setting of
the slide rule in each instance, you can get areas of circles
from their diameters, transform inches to centimeters,
quarts to liters, pounds to kilograms, and do hundreds of
other time-saving operations.

Slide rules are used in all engineering work and most
branches of science. They are being used more and more
in business today because they save hours of tedious work
in multiplication and division, and also because they are
light and small and will fit into your pocket. The better
grades of slide rules sell anywhere from five to twenty-five

---

* This section has been reprinted from *Fun with Mathematics,* by
Jerome S. Meyer, World Publishing Company, 1963.

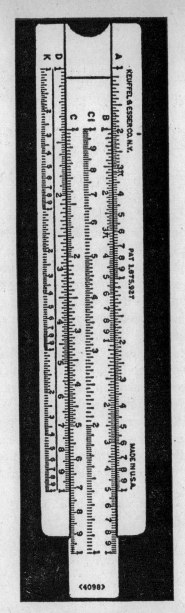

FIGURE 20

dollars, but here is a way to make yourself an excellent slide rule with an ordinary ruler, the kind you buy at the ten-cent store. If you are careful you will be surprised how accurate your homemade slide rule will be, and you will be able to multiply, divide, take square and cube roots, do ratio and proportion, raise to powers, and perform lots of other computations just by moving a strip of paper back and forth over another sheet of paper.

All you need for your homemade slide rule are two sheets of good drawing paper (bristol board is excellent), a very sharp, hard pencil (No. 3H will do), a ruler, and a little care. A magnifying glass will help, but it is not absolutely necessary if you take great care and are precise in making the first three marks on your slide rule. The accuracy of your rule will depend upon these first three marks, so it is essential that you make them with the utmost precision.

The first thing to do is to draw a line *exactly* 6¼ inches long. Mark each end of this line with very thin vertical lines and call each end 1. The left end is the "lower 1" and the right end is the "upper 1." Be sure that the distance between these two marks is *exactly* 6¼ inches—no more and no less. Now measure off *exactly* 1⅞ inches from the lower 1, make another thin vertical mark, and call it 2. This is shown in Figure 21A. Then measure *exactly* $2^{31}\!/_{32}$ inches from the lower 1; make a thin vertical line and call it 3. This, of course, is half of a sixteenth of an inch less than 3 inches, as shown in the diagram. Finally, make the same thin vertical mark at 5 $^9\!/_{32}$ inches and call it 7, as shown here. You now have 1, 2, 3, 7, and upper 1 on your

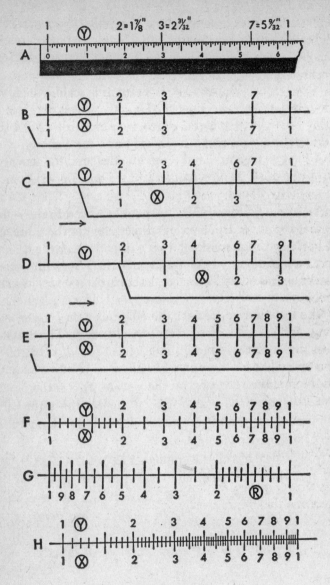

FIGURE 21

sheet. If you have marked these off with great care, your slide rule will be very useful; but if you have been careless, you may be sure that you won't get reliable readings from it.

Now refer to Figure 21B. It shows this scale, which we shall call y for convenience. Directly below it place a movable strip of paper (which we shall call x) on the line, and *very carefully* mark off the same lines on x so that the two papers, x and y, are identical and the movable strip of paper, x, also has 1, 2, 3, 7, and upper 1 on it just exactly like the y scale.

Now refer to Figure 21C. It shows x moved to the right, so that the lower 1 line on x is directly under the 2 line on y. In this position mark off 4 on y directly over the 2 on x, and 6 on y directly over the 3 on x. It is very important that these markings be exact, as shown. You now have the y scale with 1, 2, 3, 4, 6, 7, and upper 1. If you place the x scale so that lower 1 comes directly under the 4 on y, you can mark off 8 on y directly over the 2 on x. And by moving x so the 1 comes directly under the 3 on y, mark off 9 on y directly over the 3 on x (Figure 21D). Now you have all the numbers except 5 on the y scale. To get the 5, just place the 2 on the x scale directly *under* the right-hand (upper) 1 of y, and directly over the lower 1 on the x scale, and mark off 5 on scale y.

Now scale y has all the numbers 1, 2, 3, 4, 5, 6, 7, 8, 9, and the right-hand 1. Place the movable strip or scale x in the same position it was in Figure 21B and mark off the missing numbers on it. The scales should now be *identical*, as shown in Figure 21E.

At this point it is well to mark off 11 at exactly ¼ inch

from the lower 1, and 13 at exactly $2\frac{3}{32}$ inch from that 1. Here is how you fill out the rest of the slide rule, as shown in Figure 21F:

It is very important to note that although the 2, 3, 4, 5, 6, 7, 8, and 9 are unit digits, they are also 20, 30, 40, 50, 60, 70, 80, and 90, or 200, 300, 400, 500, etc. In the same way the 25, 35, 45, etc., are $2\frac{1}{2}$, $3\frac{1}{2}$, $4\frac{1}{2}$, $5\frac{1}{2}$, etc., or 250, 350, 450, 550, etc. All multiples of 10 are in the same place on the slide rule, so the decimal place makes no difference.

Place the 2 of x under the 3 of y, and mark off 1.5 or 15 above the left-hand 1 on x. Also mark off 4.5 or 45 on y directly over the 3 on x.

Place the 2 of x under the 5 of y, and mark off 2.5 or 25 above the left-hand 1 on x.

Place the 2 of x under the 7 of y, and mark of 3.5 or 35 above the left-hand 1 on x.

Place the 2 of x under the 9 of y, and mark off 4.5 or 45 above the left-hand 1 on x.

Divide the spaces between 8 and 9, and 9 and upper 1, in half for 8.5 and 9.5.

Place the left-hand 1 of x under the 11 on y, and mark off 5.5 or 55 on y above the 5 on x. Do the same for the 13 on y, and mark off 6.5 or 65 on y.

Place the left-hand 1 on x under the 15 on y, and mark off 7.5 or 75 on y directly over the 5 on x.

Place the 5 on x under the 6 on y, and mark off 1.2 or 12 on y above the left-hand 1 on x. Do the same for the 7 on y, and mark off 1.4 or 14 on y above the left-hand 1 on x.

Your upper scale now has 11, 12, 13, 14, 15 marked off in it as well as 20, 25, 30, 35, 40, 45, 50, 55, 60, 65, 70, 75, 80, 85, 90, 95, and the right-hand 1, as shown in Diagram F.

From now on it is easy. Place the left-hand 1 successively under 11, 12, 13, and use the 2 mark on the x scale to mark off

22, 24, 26, and 28 between the 2 and 3 on y. To get 16, 17, 18, and 19 on y, place the 5 on x under the 95, 90, 85, and 80 of y respectively, and mark off 19, 18, 17, and 16 above the left-hand 1 on x.

Now, as before, you can get 32, 34, 36, and 38 the way you got 22, 24, 26, and 28. Smaller divisions may be done by the eye.

By now the y scale is fairly complete, and it won't take much more work to complete it entirely. This done, mark off all the same spacing on the x scale so that you have two identical scales as shown in Figure 21H. Now you are ready to use the homemade slide rule.

If you want to expand your work and add more features to your slide rule, all you need do is make an exact duplicate of the x or y scale, turn it upside down, and number it as before. Place this new scale, which we shall call the r scale, directly under the x scale as shown in Figure 21G, and you have all the decimal equivalents by direct reading. You can see at once that if all the numbers are fractions and the 2, 3, 4, 5, etc., become ½, ⅓, ¼, ⅕ and so on, then ½ on the x scale comes directly over .5 on the r scale, and ¼ on the x scale comes to .25 on the r scale. In the same way you can read off all the fractions as decimal equivalents; thus from the diagram we get ½ is .5, ⅓ is .333, ¼ is .25, ⅕ is .2, ⅙ is .166, ⅐ is .141, ⅛ is .125 and ⅑ is .111, etc.

This r scale is the reciprocal scale, and it is nothing more than the regular scale reversed. You can multiply numbers by means of this scale by doing just the reverse of what you do with the x scale. To multiply 3 by 15 with x and y scales, you put the 1 of the x scale under the 3 of the y scale and look above 15 on the x scale to find 45 on the y scale. It's just the other way with the r scale. Here you put the 3 of

64

the r scale over the 15 of the x scale and look under the right-hand 1 of the r scale. You will find 45 on the y scale.

If you are ambitious enough to make another scale from the x or y scale, and make it just twice as large, or 12½ inches long, by laying off exactly twice the distances on the 12½-inch line that you did on the 6¼-inch line, and then place two x scales directly above the new scale, you will see that everything on the two x scales (side by side) will be the *square* of everything on the new scale.

The slide rule that you have now made is the mathematical equivalent of commercial slide rules costing one dollar or more. Of course the commercial slide rules are more accurate than yours because they are made by machine, and are more convenient because they are made of wood, plastic, or metal. In addition, a commercial slide rule will have scales for squaring, cubing, and extracting square and cube roots, as well as for sines, cosines, tangents, logarithms, and many other functions. The y scale on your slide rule is usually called the d scale. The x scale is called the c scale, and the r scale the ci or *c-inverted* scale.

How to Use Your Slide Rule

To multiply on the slide rule, you must use either of the two 1's on the x scale and apply them under the number you want to multiply on the y scale. You must also remember that everything on the slide rule scale is a power of 10, and it is up to you to supply the proper decimal place. You know very well that 16×20, for example, is not 32 but 320. It will be at 3.2 on the scale, so it is up to you to give it the proper decimal place. Similarly, 51×60 will show up as 3.06 on the scale. You know very well that it is in the thousands, so it must be 3060. If you remember the decimal part of the slide rule, you will have no trouble at all. One more thing: this homemade slide rule, no matter how carefully you have made it, will not be accurate to four or even three decimal places. To multiply 17 by 38, for example, you know that it must end in 6, since 7×8 is 56. It is up to you to supply the last digit— the slide rule will supply the first two.

Now that you have made your slide rule so that it resembles Figure 20 (the five marks can be eliminated after 5 and the submarks are in two's), multiply 14 by 27. Move the 1 on the x scale directly under the 14 (the fourth division after the 1, which is 1.4) on the y scale and, directly above the 27 (2.7) on the y scale, read 3.7 "nearly 3.8." Now you know that the result ends in 8, so the answer must be 378, which it is.

Try another example: Multiply 53 by 23. Move the upper right 1 on the x scale directly under the 53 on the y scale and, directly over the 23 on the x scale, read 1.2 "and a little bit over." Now you know that 20×50 is 1000, so the result must be about 1200. We know that it ends in 9 since $3 \times 3 = 9$, and it is about one fifth of the way between 1.2 and 1.3. It must therefore be 1219. Now try these: 13×41, 22×17, 16×41, 31×15, 19×38.

Of course division is just the opposite. To divide 48 by 4, just place the 4 on the x scale directly under the 4.8 on the y scale and refer back to the left 1 on x. Directly above it read 1.2, which of course is 12 in this case. Divide 65 by 22: Move the 2.2 on the x scale directly under the 6.5 (halfway between the 6 and 7) on the y scale and, over the left-hand 1 on the x scale, read 2.95. Divide 13 by 2: move the 1.3 on the x scale under the 2 on the y scale and, over the right-hand 1 on x, read 6.5. Now try the following for practice: $64 \div 32$, $87 \div 3$, $14 \div 7$, $734 \div 12$.

Proportions are easy on the slide rule. Try the following: $3 : 5 = 7 : ?$ Move the 3 on x under the 5 on y, and over the 6 on x read upper 1 (10) on y. Now move this 6 on x under the left-hand 1 on y, and, over 7 on x, read 11.75. Study this awhile, and you will see that once you have the x scale set against the y scale at any ratio, all the numbers on both these scales will be the same ratio. Set 2 under 3, and see 4 under 6, 6 under 9, and so on.

Things to Do and Make

Enlarging and Reducing

To ENLARGE OR REDUCE a photograph or drawing, apply the law of inverse squares, as shown in Figure 22. If you want to make a drawing twice or three times the size of the original, for example, the most practical method is to put the drawing under a piece of tracing paper and carefully rule off squares to some convenient fraction of an inch, depending on the size of the original drawing.

Let us suppose that the vertical and horizontal side are divided into quarter inches, and lines are drawn so as to make squares, each square being ¼ inch on a side. The next thing to do is to label all the vertical lines with letters and all the horizontal lines with numbers. Now decide whether you want your drawing to be twice or

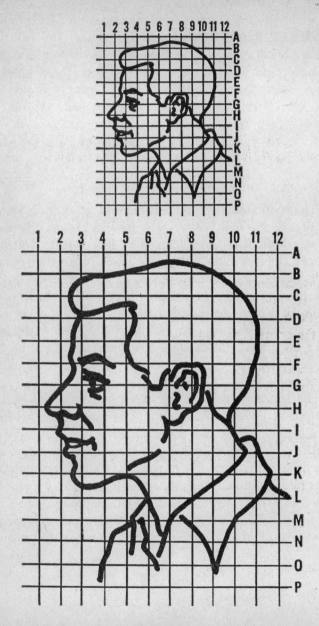

FIGURE 22

three times the original size, and make a similar chart with similar squares ½ or ¾ inch on a side. You will now have a small cross section of squares ¼ inch on a side, and a large cross section of squares twice or three times as large. Lettering and numbering these exactly as you did the smaller diagram, you can begin to copy the outline as it goes from one square to another, and in that way get a perfect enlargement of the original. Use the same method—in reverse—for reducing a picture.

Homemade Date Finder

To produce this you have to do a little work, as shown in Figure 23. The first thing is to select a smooth piece of wood about ½ inch thick and 2½ inches wide. Cut two pieces, the first 8 inches long (the base of the date chart) and the second at least 5 inches long. Now make an accurate copy of the chart shown here and carefully paste it on the 8-inch piece so that the line *AB* falls more than an inch from the lower edge of the 8-inch piece. After you have done this, you must make a shadow piece from the 5-inch wood strip and lay it exactly on the line *AB* and at right angles to it.

The length of this shadow piece is determined by the latitude of your home, so you will have to consult an atlas or almanac to find out approximately what latitude on earth you happen to be living in. Fractions of a degree are not necessary. If you live in New York City, your latitude is 41 degrees; if you live in Los Angeles, it is 34 degrees. Be sure you know your right latitude before proceeding. Now refer to the lines at the bottom of the chart. Each line represents a different latitude, and it is up to you to measure

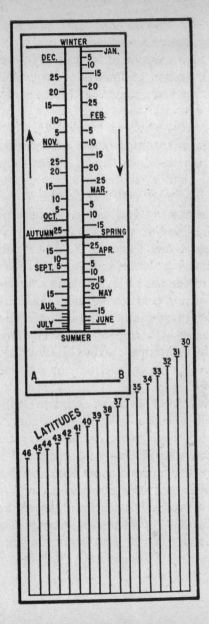

FIGURE 23

the lines of your latitude and mark it off on the shadow piece. Be sure your marking is exact; then cut the shadow piece precisely to that length and lay it on the date finder. If your work is correct, when you put this little stick in the noon sun its shadow will point to the current date.

Make Your Own Sundial

Here is the way to make an excellent sundial that will keep good time on sunny days. The first thing to do is to determine the latitude of the place where you live. Having done that, draw a straight horizontal line and lay off this latitude (the angle ϕ) by drawing the right triangle shown in Figure 24A. Now draw two circles—one with the base of the triangle as a radius, and the other with the hypotenuse as a radius. Draw a vertical line through the center of these circles and divide the vertical diameter of the smaller circle into five equal parts. Now, count down three of these divisions and draw the horizontal line *DE*, as shown in Figure 24B. Divide the arc *DE* into twelve equal parts and connect each part with the point *O*. Through each division, draw horizontal lines parallel to *DE*, and from the intersection of the radial lines with the smaller circle draw vertical lines forming a series of small right triangles as shown. All these lines must be done in light pencil, so they may be easily erased. Now, from point *O*, draw lines that pass through each of these right angles and intersect the circumference of the large circle. These twelve marks will be your number points on the finished sundial.

The horizontal line *DE* will now become the 6 A.M. and 6 P.M. line, and the twelve marks you just made by the twelve lines passing through the right angles and intersecting the large circumference will be the progressive hours

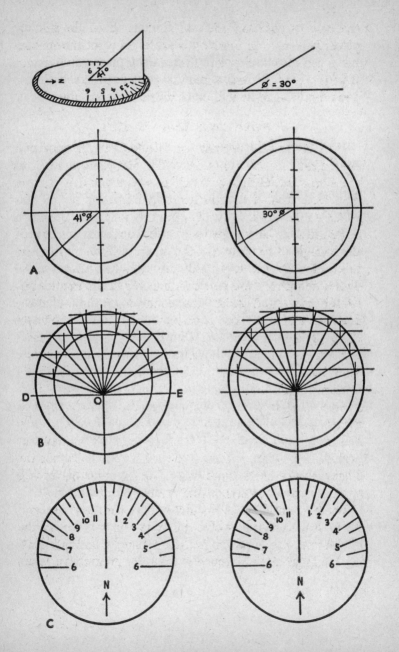

FIGURE 24

7, 8, 9, 10, etc. all the way round the dial. The noon line is the vertical line. By placing on this line a right triangular marker whose angle is the latitude of the place you live in, as shown, you will have a sundial that keeps good time. Be sure to point the noon line to the north when you place the dial in the sun. The finished dial in the figure is divided into half-hours.

To the right of the diagrams A, B, and C we see another sundial which is figured for a latitude of 30 degrees.

Dividing Lines and Circles into Equal Parts and Ratios

It is surprising how few people apply a simple proposition in plane geometry to the practical problem of dividing a line into a given number of equal parts, as shown in Figure 25. It is a simple matter if you have a line of 6 inches to divide into twelve equal parts. It just means making a mark at every half-inch point. But suppose the line is $5\frac{3}{16}$ inches long, and you are required to divide it into eleven equal parts. Are you going to divide 11 into $5\frac{3}{16}$ and then measure out each of these divisions? That would be foolish when a proposition in geometry states that "if parallels intercept equal lengths on one transversal, they intercept equal lengths on all transversals." Taking advantage of this fact, all you need to do is draw a line from the left extremity of the given line in any direction and mark off equal divisions on it—in this case eleven half-inches. Now join the end of this line to the right extremity of the given line, and draw lines through each point parallel to this line, as shown. The intersection of these parallel lines with the given line divide the given line into eleven equal parts.

74

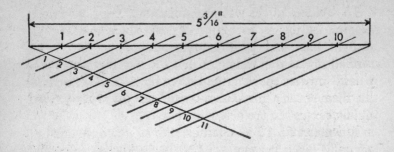

FIGURE 25

Suppose you want to divide an odd-length line in half, quarters, and eighths, in that ratio. Instead of figuring out the problem arithmetically, apply the same rule as before. Draw a line from the left extremity of the given line and make it an even number of inches—say 4 or 6. It is a simple matter to divide this line in half, quarters, and eighths; then join its extremity to the right extremity of the given line and proceed as before. See Figure 26.

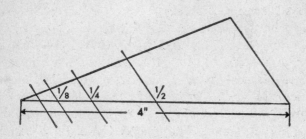

FIGURE 26

To divide a circle into any number of equal parts—for example seven, as in Figure 27—use the diameter as a straight line, and by the same method previously described divide that diameter into the required number of parts. Now pay special attention to the *second* division on the diameter. Taking B as a center and the diameter as a radius, project an arc below the circle, as shown. Taking A as a center and AB as a radius, project another arc. Both arcs will meet at some point O below the circle. A line drawn from O through the second division and projected to meet the circumference at C will be one of the required number of parts.

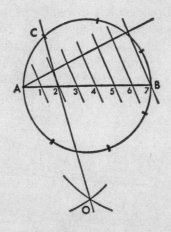

FIGURE 27

Some Tricky Puzzles

H<small>ERE ARE SOME PUZZLES</small> to try your wits and patience. If you give up, or just want to check your results, the answers are given on pages 85 to 88.

Right on the Dot

Figure 28 shows four dots with instructions in the middle. You are to make a perfect square as directed.

CAN YOU DRAW A PERFECT
SQUARE HAVING ONE DOT
ON EACH OF ITS 4 SIDES
BUT NO SIDE IS TO TOUCH
ANY OF THE WORDS WHICH
ARE PRINTED HEREIN? IT
IS NOT AS EASY AS IT MAY
APPEAR AT FIRST GLANCE.

F<small>IGURE</small> 28

Merry-go-round

Can you place the first eleven numbers in Figure 29 in the eleven circles so that every three numbers in a straight line add up to 18?

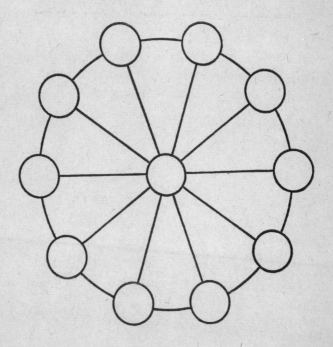

FIGURE 29

Straight-line Quarter Circle

Using Figure 30, draw a quarter circle with a ruler, making each straight line longer than 2 inches.

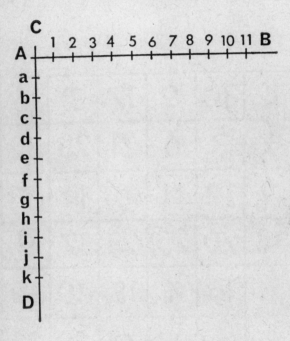

FIGURE 30

The 50 Puzzle

Figure 31 shows a square with thirty-six boxes containing numbers that have been picked at random. In the shortest time possible, you are to connect any three boxes that touch each other at some point—horizontally, vertically, or diagonally—and whose numbers add up to 50. It's not as easy at it looks!

12	30	9	17	31	16
7	3	6	21	23	32
2	19	11	8	14	7
13	20	25	28	17	9
26	16	4	18	10	30
1	5	27	9	29	33

FIGURE 31

Quintuplets on the Square

Can you transform Figure 32 into five small squares, all equal to one another, and their total area equal to the area of the given square?

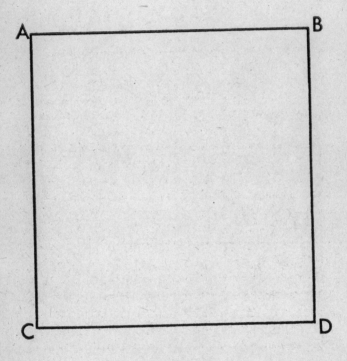

FIGURE 32

It's Easy When You Know How

Divide the circle in Figure 33 into four equal parts by drawing three curved lines of equal length.

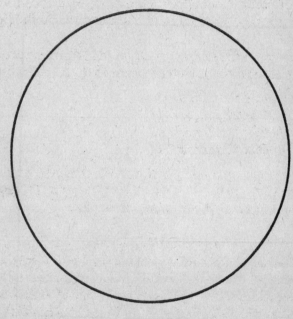

FIGURE 33

Juggling Numbers

1. What is the smallest number which, when multiplied by 2 and adding 2 to the product, has its digits reversed? For example, if ab represents the digits, then $2(ab) + 2 = ba$. (**Hint:** The number must have at least two digits and be less than 50.)

2. What five-digit number, when multiplied by 4, has its digits reversed? For example, if the digits are $a, b, c, d,$ and e, then $abcde \times 4 = edcba$. (Note that the middle digit remains c.)

3. You may add, subtract, multiply, and divide, use fractions or decimals or any other means to do the following:

    (a) Make 100 with four 7's.
    (b) Make 20 with two 3's.
    (c) Make 7 with four 2's.
    (d) Make 37 with six 6's.

For example, to make 100 with six 9's, combine the 9's as follows: $99 + 99/99$. To make 1000 with eight 8's, group the 8's in this way: $8 + 8 + 8 + 88 + 888$.

Three Strange Queries

1. The size of a book is approximately 6 by 9 inches, and each page is of normal thickness. Suppose you had a sheet of paper and cut it in half, then cut that half in half, and kept on cutting into halves thirty times, finally piling all these sheets one on top of the other. How large would the sheet of paper have to be to begin with in order to have the final cutting 6 by 9 inches, and how high would the pile be after thirty cuttings?

2. They say that the albatross is the world's largest fly-ing bird, with a wingspread of about 12 feet. Assume two identical albatrosses flying over an empty cement parking lot at noon. One albatross is only 10 feet above the road-way, while the other flies at a height of 250 feet. If both birds cast a shadow on the roadway, which one's shadow will be the longer?

3. A boat is anchored in a bay, and a rope ladder hangs loosely down from the railing to the edge of the water. The distance between each rung of the ladder is 1 foot, and there are ten rungs showing. Assuming that the tide comes in at the rate of 1.37 feet per hour, how many rungs will be showing after 4.8 hours?

Answers

Right on the Dot:

CAN YOU DRAW A PERFECT SQUARE HAVING ONE DOT ON EACH OF ITS 4 SIDES BUT NO SIDE IS TO TOUCH ANY OF THE WORDS WHICH ARE PRINTED HEREIN? IT IS NOT AS EASY AS IT MAY APPEAR AT FIRST GLANCE.

Merry-go-round:

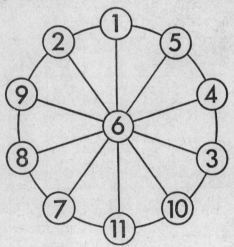

Straight-line Quarter Circle. Connect numbers on *AB* with letters on *CD* as shown: 1-*k*, 2-*j*, 3-*i*, 4-*h*, 5-*g*, 6-*f*, 7-*e*, 8-*d*, 8-*c*, 10-*b*, 11-*a*. You will find that the intersections of these lines form a perfect quarter circle.

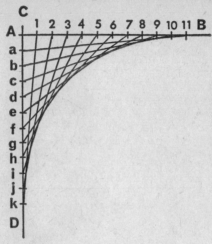

The Fifty Puzzle:

12	30	9	17	31	16
7	3	6	21	23	32
2	19	11	8	14	7
13	20	25	28	17	9
26	16	4	18	10	30
1	5	27	9	29	33

Quintuplets on the Square. Bisect the sides of the square in E, F, G, and H, and draw lines as shown. The square *ABCD* will then be transformed into five equal squares.

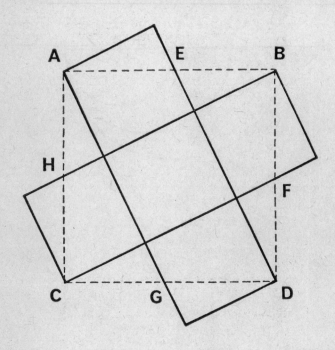

It's Easy When You Know How. Divide diameter *AB* into four parts as shown and draw semicircles on *A-C, A-D, A-E, B-E, B-D,* and *B-C.* You have now drawn three equal lines and divided the circle into four equal parts, as shown in diagram on next page.

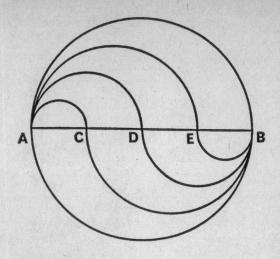

Juggling Numbers:
1. 25
2. 21978 × 4 = 87912
3. (a) 77/.77 = 100
   (b) 3!/.3 = 20 (Remember 3! = 1 × 2 × 3 = 6.)
   (c) $\dfrac{2/.2}{2} + 2 = 7$
   (d) $6 \times 6 + \dfrac{66}{66} = 37$

Three Strange Queries:

1. The original sheet of paper would have to be 16 square miles in area, and after thirty cuttings the pile would be more than 25 miles high.

2. There could be no measurable difference in the two shadows, since the light source in 93,000,000 miles away.

3. Ten rungs. The boat rises with the incoming tide.